Hampshire's
Countryside Heritage
HEATHLAND

Acknowledgments

The County Planning Department gratefully acknowledges the assistance of the many organisations and individuals who have helped in the preparation of this booklet and in particular the Institute of Terrestrial Ecology (Dr. S. B. Chapman); the Nature Conservancy Council (C. R. Tubbs, Dr. R. B. Gibbons, Dr. R. J. Hornby); and the Ministry of Defence (Lt.-Colonel C. N. Clayden (Retd.)).

Produced in the County Planning Department

Written by Vernon Hazel

Designed and Illustrated by Deborah Gandy

Based on a report by Dr. S. B. Chapman

Photographs by Bob Gibbons, Peter Wilson
and Phil Colebourn

Printed by Hampshire County Council

2nd Impression 1984

ISBN 0 900908 77 7

Hampshire's Countryside Heritage

HEATHLAND

Preface

The booklet is one of a series about countryside features being studied by the County Planning Department as part of its Countryside Heritage Project.

The Culmination of this project will be the production of a 'Countryside Heritage Policy' indicating policies and priorities for the conservation of Hampshire's countryside.

Even when the Countryside Heritage Policy is published a great deal of information and study will still be required. One of the purposes of this booklet is to stimulate interest in Hampshire's heathland with a view to encouraging individuals and groups of people to become heathland enthusiasts and guardians.

Contents

1. *Burton Common*

A typical heathland scene

Introduction

The County Council intends to conserve threatened natural habitats to maintain an attractive and diverse countryside. The purpose of this booklet is to draw attention to the extent of heathland and its value to the people of Hampshire.

The effect of heathland on man has been powerful, and a number of writers have tried to capture its qualities. Few have done it with such feeling as Thomas Hardy in one of his more evocative passages, describing Egdon Heath, in "The Return of the Native".

> "Twilight combined with the scenery of Egdon Heath to evolve a thing majestic without severity, impressive without showiness, emphatic in admonitions, grand in its simplicity."

Hampshire's heathland, though less extensive and dramatic than that in some counties, nevertheless provides:—

diverse and attractive scenery;

examples of farming practice from days gone by;

food, protection and breeding areas for threatened birds, animals and insects;

a resource for scientific and historic research;

open space for recreation, and food for livestock and fuel for man.

The extent of heathland in Hampshire is shrinking; if it is lost the Hampshire countryside heritage will be the poorer. To most people heathland generally conveys a picture of heather, especially when a mass of purple flowers in late summer. The word 'heather' is often used to refer to dwarf scrub vegetation including heather or ling, bell heather and cross-leaved heath and other ericacious plants. These areas are becoming scarce, so that other areas, are now considered to fall within this definition. In this booklet heathland refers to impoverished soil covered by heather and other dwarf vegetation, relatively free from trees but often containing scrub, gorse and bracken. Associated with heathlands, and exhibiting many of its characteristics, are acid grasslands, valley bogs, and, occasionally, chalk heath.

Converting heathland into agricultural land circa 1100/1200

The History of Heathland in Hampshire

Today's heathland is a link with the past. It is a relic of prehistoric and historic farming practices which once flourished here. The story of heathland in Hampshire provides an interesting footnote to the county's social and economic history.

The Origin of Heathland

The development of techniques of pollen analysis[1] and the other studies in vegetational history have helped to explain the origins of heathland. The areas of heathland vegetation expanded as man changed from nomadic hunter-gatherer to farmer and cleared the forest. Godwin[2], Dimbleby[3] and, more locally, Haskins[4] and Barber[5] and other workers from Southampton University have demonstrated how woodland declined and heathland vegetation became more widely distributed in Neolithic times. Heathland had probably become an important feature of the landscape by the late Bronze Age.

After the Bronze Age the area of woodland decreased still further as man tried to clear more land for grazing. Sooner or later, depending on the nature of the soil and the rate of its impoverishment, this clearance led to an increase in the area of heathland.

As society became more sophisticated an agricultural economy developed which encouraged the preservation of heath on waste and common land for its grazing value. Later the creation of royal forests as hunting preserves, by keeping land open for deer, grazing and the chase also allowed further large areas of heathland to be preserved.

Wastes and Commons

The pre-enclosure system of farming, which was known to have existed in Wessex in the seventh century, had five categories of land:— arable, pasture, meadow, forest and waste. The heathlands which survive today do so mainly because of the value attributed to the wastes and commons of which they were part. Much of the waste-lands were fen, marsh, wood and heath. They supplied villages with supplementary feed for livestock, and with timber, fuel and other useful commodities on a common basis.

From the pre-enclosure system of farming there evolved well-defined and documented 'rights of commons'. A right of common is defined by Taverner[6] as "a right which one or more persons may have to take or use

Loading turf cut for fuel

some portion of that which another person's soil naturally produces or contains." It applies to the taking of various forms of food, fuel, bedding and fencing materials, many with unusual names, e.g. estovers, turbary and piscary (the rights to take wood for various reasons, to dig or cut turf for fuel and to take fish from ponds and streams). A number of these rights apply to heathland.

The taking of common lands and wastes into private ownership became an established practice at an early date, probably during the sixth century. By the thirteenth century most had passed into the private ownership of the Lords of the Manor. It is not apparent how or why this change took place but it resulted in the peasantry retaining only its customary rights over the surface of the land.

In the twelfth and thirteenth centuries there was a marked increase in the population, and large tracts of remaining 'waste' lands were brought into cultivation to meet the demands of the expanding population. A large number of farms was created on the waste lands by means of licences granted by the Lord of the Manor.

The real impetus for changing the countryside came about in 1350, partly as a result of the Black Death. The disappearance of whole families and large portions of villages enabled surviving Lords of the Manor to appropriate holdings in common fields and wastes for their own use. Despite all these encroachments on remaining manorial wastes and commons, Gregory King, in a survey of land use in 1688, indicated that one quarter of the land in England and Wales was still waste (heath, moor, mountain and barren land including, in the lowlands, areas of infertile soils).

In the seventeenth century enclosure by private agreement proceeded apace. Much of Hampshire was enclosed by this means during the late sixteenth century and throughout the seventeenth. Meagre (1697), Defoe (1724) and Arthur Young (1768 and 1771) all remarked on the extent of enclosures in the county.

Enclosure by private Acts of Parliament commenced with the first Act in 1709 but did not really gain momentum until 1765 to 1785, when on average some 47 Acts were passed each year. However, the Driver brothers in their County Agricultural Survey of 1792 recorded some extensive tracts of open heath and uncultivated land, e.g. East Woodhay, Newbury; Kingsclere; Froxfield; Barnet Common; Botley; Waltham Chase, and the Hampshire part of Bagshot Heath. In 1792 the total area of wasteland (excluding forests) in Hampshire was about 46,540 hectares.

To assist private enclosure and improve food production from areas still remaining under the open field system, the first General Enclosure Act was passed in 1801 and a number then followed up to 1882. Between 1709 and 1801, 16,916 hectares had been enclosed by 35 private Acts. In the next 75 years a further 14,974 hectares were enclosed under these Acts. The changing scene is recorded in many parish and manor records, eg:

"A few mud cottages on an unenclosed common tenanted by labourers and squatters have, since the inclosures of Botley Common in 1863, become the populus and thriving village of Hedge End"[7]

In 1873 Parliament requested information about the extent of remaining commons and common field lands. The returns related to the parishes of each county, and in the County of Southampton (excluding the Isle of Wight and the New Forest) it was recorded that 16,796 hectares remained as commons, much of which could have been heathland.

A typical New Forest heathland scene

When Taverner surveyed the commons of Hampshire, excluding the New Forest and the County Boroughs of Portsmouth, Southampton and Bournemouth, in 1956 he recorded a total of more than 6,270 hectares in some 138 commons. Exactly what proportion of these remaining commons was heathlands is not easy to determine. Indeed, it is difficult to relate any of the surveys quoted because of the differences in the criteria used and the general credibility of the results obtained. Some surveys once held to be reliable are now known to be unreliable in whole or part.

Enclosure of wastes and commons, in the manner outlined above, has brought about the destruction of heathland due to the subsequent improvement of the land for agriculture, or its planting with trees. The technique of clearance for agriculture was very often paring, as a preliminary to burning. Paring involved the use of an instrument known as a "breast plough" by which a labourer could cut and turn a sod of some 1' x 1½" x 3', which was later burnt.

Royal Forests
There were, in medieval times, all or part of eleven Royal Forests* in Hampshire. Only the New Forest and Woolmer Forest retain any significant areas of heathland.

3

The Royal forests evolved their own distinctive forest laws, like the Charta de Foresta of 1217. This legislation dealt primarily with disafforestation and outlined the legal framework for the enclosure and cultivation of private lands in Royal forests under licence from the Crown, which had hitherto been illegal. Despite legislative pressure to protect woodlands for the benefit of deer, provide more timber for the Navy and eventually to remove deer to increase the area of pasture for commoners' livestock, there is evidence[8] that the proportions of woodland and heathland today are similar to that in Roman times. However, there were wide fluctuations in these proportions over the period between the Roman occupation and 1450, when the woodland area increased substantially, between 1450 and 1850 when it declined, and since 1850, when there has been some expansion.

The fact that extensive areas of heathland remain in the New Forest is in no small part due to the lack of enforcement of Forest laws by local Crown officials (regarders, agisters, etc.). The former acquiesced in small-scale additional Forest clearance, while the latter countenanced over-grazing in their own interests. Rights of Common (pasture, marl, estovers etc.,) are unique in the New Forest as they were Statutorily Registered in 1851 and remain so today. Grazing rights have been jealously guarded by the commoners, and latterly by

A Kestrel on grassy heath.

the verderers on their behalf. Insistence on retaining rights of common has prevented the improvement of extensive areas of the New Forest to the advantage of the heathland vegetation. Only as a wartime emergency, when there was instituted the New Forest Pastoral Development Scheme, have there been attempts to plough, fertilise and re-seed significant areas. The wartime scheme was designed to improve some 364 hectares on fifteen sites. The first of these were Ober Heath, Longcross Plain and Long Bottom, which were not enclosed and were re-seeded with barn sweepings. The level of improvement achieved on these first three

sites is not as good as on those treated subsequently, which were enclosed and re-seeded with appropriate seed mixtures. Overall the scheme was successful and nearly all the 364 hectares of grassland remain as a result of this scheme.

Under the New Forest Act 1949 the Commission was empowered, with the consent of the verderers, to enclose for planting with trees a further 2,024 hectares of the open Forest. The verderers gave their consent in 1958 to the enclosure of 809 hectares, mainly as an amenity to counter the visual effect of the building of Fawley Refinery. It is doubtful whether they, or public opinion, would now allow the remaining 1,214 hectares to be enclosed. Open Forest, containing heathland, is thus being safeguarded.

Woolmer Forest, like other Royal forests, came under the direct control of the Crown. The Crown's interest in this Forest declined during the fourteenth century and was only resumed when timber was required for naval use or land required for enclosure and cultivation. The change that has taken place in this part of East Hampshire can be seen by comparing the situation today, when only one square mile of Woolmer Forest remains, with that of the description of Gilbert White in 1789.[9]

> "The Royal Forest of Wolmer is a tract of land about 7 miles in length by 2½ in breadth, running nearly from north to south, and is abutted on, to begin to the south, and so to proceed eastward, by the parishes of Greatham, Lysse, Rogate and Trotton, in the County of Sussex; by Bramshott, Hedleigh and Kingsley. This Royalty consists entirely of sand covered with heath and fern; but is somewhat diversified with hills and dales, without having one standing tree in the whole extent. In the bottoms, where the waters stagnate, are many bogs, which formerly abounded with subterraneous trees. . ."

Another large area of heathland, enclosed and freed of any rights of common, has survived at Bramshott Common. Smaller remains of the original Woolmer Forest survive as a result of public ownership: Broxhead Common in Whitehill and Headley parishes (Ministry of Defence/County Council), Slab Common in Whitehill parish (Ministry of Defence), Kingsley Common in Kingsley parish (Ministry of Defence) and Shortheath Common in Worldham parish (Ministry of Defence).

Ludshott Common, also in the Parish of Bramshott, and containing an extensive area of heathland, survives because of its control by the National Trust.

Despite enclosure and removal of common rights, ownership by the Forestry Commission, Ministry of Defence, or other public bodies will secure the future of the heathland by preventing encroachment for development or agriculture and generally securing an appropriate form of management.

Heathland Today

In recent years a new force has emerged, through increased public use of, and interest in, the countryside which has counter-balanced pressures by farming, forestry and development interests. Open space and

Woodland encroaching onto heathland.

wildlife habitats close to large areas of population now have many defenders among conservationists.

The map on page 7 compares the extent of heathland now with that in 1810, when the first editions of the Ordnance Survey maps were prepared. In 1810 there were some 37,000 hectares of heath in Hampshire. In 1982 it is likely that barely 18,000 hectares remain as recognisable heathland. Much of the heathland which remains does so because it is protected by public ownership. Major owners of heathland in Hampshire are the Crown and the Ministry of Defence, for whom the Forestry Commission and Property Services Agency act as agents. Other significant owners include the County Council and the National Trust.

The value of heathland as open space was recognised during the early part of the nineteenth century when some of the social disadvantages of the enclosure of commons became apparent, especially where they abutted or formed part of developing urban areas. Cobbett for example commented:[10]

> "The cottagers produce from their little bits, in food for themselves, and in things to be sold at market, more than any neighbouring farm of 200 acres. . . I learnt to hate a system that could lead English gentlemen to disregard matters like these! That could induce them to tear up 'waste' and sweep away its occupiers like those I have described! Wastes indeed! . . . . Was it a 'waste when 100, perhaps, of healthy boys and girls were playing there of a Sunday, instead of creeping about covered with filth in alleys of a town?"

Pressure for the use of remaining heathland and commons (both urban and rural) as public open space gave rise to the formation of the first 'conservation' pressure group in 1865. This was the Commons, Open Spaces and Footpaths Preservation Society which aimed to prevent enclosure of, and encroachment on, commons and open spaces.

Unfortunately the attractiveness of heathlands brings its own problems. Commons such as Broxhead and Yateley are under considerable recreational pressure, and the resulting damage to ground flora and surface soil is often apparent, even when vehicles are excluded. In the New Forest, where it has long been accepted that the public has a right to roam at will in the unenclosed areas, the problems caused by day visitors coming by car resulted in a joint study in the late 1960s and early 1970s[11]. The Forestry Commission implemented the final recommendations of that study and has thereby, so far, successfully controlled day visitors to the New Forest.

On the other hand, where there is not sufficient use by the public to prevent scrub from developing, or remaining areas of heathland are too small or fragmented to be used for their original purpose, it is often only grazing, cutting or occasional burning which can prevent their change to woodland.

*Ancient Woodlands: Hampshire County Planning Department, 1983.

A mixture of valley bog and dry heathland

The Occurrence and Distribution of Heathland

Heathland only evolved naturally in a few coastal locations where a combination of poor soils, humid climate and exposure to winds from the sea ensured that only low, scrubby vegetation could survive. Elsewhere its emergence and maintenance depended on the activities of man.

Ling *(Calluna)* and other ericaceous heathland requires certain conditions to become established. The soil should be low in levels of plant nutrients and have a low pH value* within the range of 3.5 to 6.7. Fortunately, once established, Ling will exacerbate soil deterioration thus providing the desired conditions. There must be a mild damp climate with no great seasonal fluctuations and there must be enough light.

Landform and drainage cause differences in soil moisture which produce variations within heathland vegetation. There are dry heaths, wet heaths, humid heaths, valley bogs and even, in some instances, heaths on chalk soils. For the development and survival of the wetter heathland vegetation types, which occur in low-lying areas and at seepage points between permeable and impermeable strata on valley sides, it is important that the nutrient level of the soil is not enriched as a result of drainage from other areas.

Once heathland vegetation is established there must be some mechanism, for example burning or grazing, to destroy young trees and shrubs and thus prevent the natural change of heathland to scrub and woodland.

Heathland in Western Europe
The extent of heathland in Europe is shown on the accompanying map. Twenty-one types of heathland have been recognised in Europe. The best examples are in Spain, France, Ireland and Britain. Many are mountain

bogs and moors exhibiting different characteristics from the lowland Atlantic-type heath of southern England.

In Europe heathland reached a peak in extent and value for pastoral farming and ancillary timber production during the sixteenth century. By the first half of the

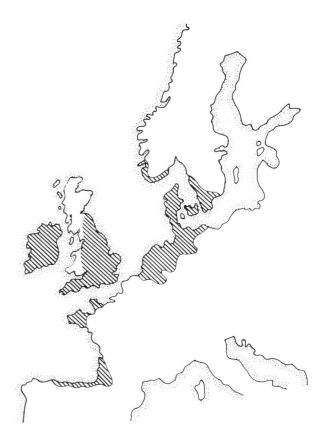

The lowland heathland region of Western Europe.

nineteenth century it was in decline. This decline was due to enclosure of some land and increasing agricultural output resulting from improvements, especially the use of manure and chemical fertilisers. The competitiveness of intercontinental trade, undermining the value of production from marginal areas, furthered the decline. These changes released large areas of one-time grazing grounds, including some lowland heathland, for new uses or to revert to woodland.

Heathland in Europe has been declining even more rapidly in recent years.[12] This loss prompted the Council of Europe in 1979 to give more priority to the designation of heathland reserves. It continues to be under threat from development, agriculture, forestry, mineral extraction, recreation and natural colonisation by scrub and trees.

In Britain, as elsewhere in Europe, the area has declined significantly. The overall distribution of heathland, moorland and associated vegetation types in Britain has been shown on maps such as the 1:625 000 Vegetation Maps published by the Ordnance Survey in 1945 and 1953, and in the Oxford Atlas of Britain published in 1963. The various editions of the Land Utilisation Survey also give some indications of heathland vegetation with their 'heath, moorland and rough land' category.

Britain has nine of the twenty-one types of heathland found in Europe. In the uplands large tracts of moorland still remain, representing 57.6 per cent and 32.7 per cent of the total land areas of Scotland and Wales respectively, despite many claims upon them for afforestation or improved forms of agriculture.

Heathland, of the type found in Hampshire, is the lowland equivalent of moorland, which covers much of the uplands in Great Britain. This heathland is important because it occurs in areas with a better climate. It therefore supports a range of plants, animals and insects not to be found in the cooler wetter and more exposed uplands. Thus the vast areas of upland moorland which remain are no substitute for lowland heathland.

However, lowland heathland, once widely distributed throughout Britain where there were suitable soils, is now greatly reduced in area. Dry heathland in particular is under threat as, being well drained, it is more likely

areas of existing heathland
areas of former heathland

The past and present extent of Hampshire's heathland

than wet heathland to be reclaimed for agriculture. Much of the heathland which does survive is common land. The Royal Commission on Common Land between 1955 and 1958 indicated that some 4.03 per cent of the total surface of England and Wales was common land. In Hampshire the figure is 6.25 per cent (excluding the New Forest), while in the rest of the South-East it is only 1.88 per cent. This difference is an indication of the importance of the remaining heathland in Hampshire.

The southern part of Britain is mainly influenced by wet, mild Atlantic conditions. The western half of southern England is wetter than the eastern half and the division between east and west passes approximately through eastern Dorset. As a result of these climatic differences the geographical limits of a number of heathland plant species pass through central southern England. Dorset and Hampshire have interesting variations in their dry heathland (see page 10).

The New Forest now accounts for a third of the area of lowland heath which is listed as of Grades 1 or 2 ecological significance in the Nature Conservancy Council's Nature Conservation Review.

Hampshire's Heathland

Heathland is to be found principally in three areas of the county: South Hampshire and the New Forest, the Thames Basin and the Western Weald, as shown on the accompanying map on page 9.

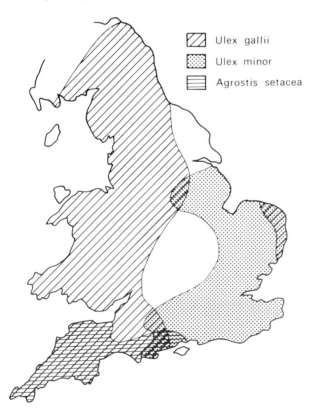

Ulex gallii

Ulex minor

Agrostis setacea

The generalised distribution of three common heathland plants.

Occasionally very small areas of chalk heath can be found (see page 12).

South Hampshire and the New Forest Area: The perambulation of the New Forest, within which the 14,370 hectares of heathland lie, extends on its western boundary from north of Fordingbridge, on the east of the Avon Valley, almost to New Milton. Its eastern boundary runs parallel to Southampton Water and the River Test from West Wellow to Blackfield. There are also small heaths which are very important, such as the 40-hectare Burton Common.

Along the coast Browndown and Chark Commons, near Gosport, are still reasonably extensive at 65 and 41 hectares respectively and they contain identifiable heathland. Further inland Shedfield Common (13 hectares) to the east of Botley, and Wickham Common (27 hectares), north of Fareham, still exhibit heathland characteristics. Baddesley Common and Emer Bog (37 hectares), north of Southampton, form an area sufficiently rich in plant and animal species to warrant the Secretary of State for the Environment intervening to safeguard the common, and the Hampshire and Isle of Wight Naturalists' Trust acquiring the bog.

The Thames Basin: Extensive areas of wet and dry heathland and acid grassland are to be found within the Hampshire part of the Thames Basin. The largest remaining area (218 hectares) is Yateley Common, astride the A30 east of Bramshill Forest. Second largest is Hazeley Heath, of some 175 hectares, north of Hartley Wintney. East of Aldershot, at Bourley Water, some 150 hectares set aside for water catchment contain a range of habitats including dry heaths and bogs. Other significant areas of heathland in the Thames Basin are Eelmore Marsh (71 hectares), to the north of Aldershot, and Silchester and Tadley Commons (69 hectares). Smaller areas, such as Pondtail, to the east of Fleet, are also important.

Remnants of former more extensive heathland are still to be found at Newtown and Burghclere Commons where an area of remarkably fine mature heather, worthy of protection and further attention, was recently rediscovered during the survey of woodland adjacent to Burghclere.

Western Weald: Only the western end of the Weald lies in Hampshire but this contains a significant amount of remaining heathland — some 842 hectares. The largest area is that of Bramshott and Ludshott Commons (378 hectares), near Liphook, which provide a very good example of open heathland. Woolmer Forest, including Woolmer Pond, the next largest area (some 241 hectares) contains some of the best examples of dry heathland.

The remaining heathlands are much smaller but still sufficiently important in many instances to be notified as Sites of Special Scientific Interest, (SSSIs). These are Conford Moor (18 hectares), Broxhead Common (35 hectares), Blackmoor (32 hectares) and Shortheath Common (60 hectares). The latter, though predominantly acid grassland, contains a particularly interesting valley bog. Other sizeable areas of former heathland still exhibiting heathland characteristics, even if now largely invaded by scrub woodland, are Kingsley Common (45 hectares) and Greatham Moor (33 hectares). These areas are remnants of Woolmer Forest, to the north and south of Whitehill respectively.

New Forest
1 Baddesley Common
2 Badminston Common
  Fields Heath
3 Browndown
4 Burton
5 Chark Common
6 Cranemoor
7 Hamble
8 New Forest area
9 Shedfield Common
10 Shelley Common
11 Sinah Common
12 Wickham

Thames Basin
13 Bartley Heath and
  Hook Common
14 Bourley Water
15 Eelmoor Marsh
16 Hazeley Heath
17 Heckfield Heath
18 Long Valley
19 Silchester Common
20 Tadley Common
21 Yateley Common

Western Weald
22 Newtown and Burghclere
  Commons
23 Blackmoor
24 Bramshott & Ludshott
25 Broxhead Common
26 Canford Moor
27 Greatham Moor
28 Kingsley Common
29 Passfield Common
30 Slab Common
31 Shortheath
32 Woolmer Forest

The distribution of Hampshire's heathland. (For further details of heathland in Hampshire see Appendix Two).

*pH is a measure of soil acidity: pH7 represents a condition
of neutrality, 7.5 is slightly alkaline and 4.5 is strongly acid.

Heather and gorse – a diminishing habitat

The Wildlife of Heathland

Those species which depend upon heathland for their existence in Hampshire include:

Mossy stonecrop
Marsh gentian
Marsh clubmoss
Wild gladiolus
Dartford warbler
Stonechat
Sand lizard
Smooth snake
Natterjack toad
Heath grasshopper
Green tiger beetle
Silver-studded blue butterfly
True lovers knot moth
Small red damsel fly

Lowland heathland is increasingly acting as a refuge for those species deprived of their preferred habitats as a result of agricultural, forestry, recreational or urban development. However, the smaller the remaining area of heathland the fewer the heathland wildlife species which remain and the lower the concentration of the surviving fauna. An area in the course of reverting to scrub and woodland supports a greater number of species, as birds, insects and plants infiltrate from adjoining agricultural land, woods and gardens. But these incoming species will generally be the more common ones and they are ultimately likely to suppress the remaining rarer heathland species.

Heathland Plants

Hampshire's heathlands are broadly classified as 'Atlantic Heather and Gorse Heaths of an Anglo-Norman type' but various sub-types can be recognised: dry heathland, humid heathland and wet heathlands. Heathland plants can also be found in valley bogs, acid grassland, chalk heath and scrub.

Dry Heathland is found on free-draining soils where the water table is below the surface at all times. It contains mainly ling, bell heather, dwarf gorse *(Ulex minor)*, European gorse and bristle-leaved bent. It is possible to find pure stands of heather but more often it is found with gorse, bristle-leaved bent, sheep's-fescue, wavy-hair grass, bilberry, common tormentil, heath-grass and bracken. In a very few places in the New Forest where slightly better soils have been colonised by bracken, and a deep acid litter has developed, wild gladiolus can still be found.

In the west of Hampshire the other type of dwarf gorse *(Ulex gallii)* is to be found, as well as certain hybrids resulting from the two types. There is a difference between the types of grasses found on dry heathland in the north-eastern and south-western parts of Hampshire. Wavy-hair grass predominates in the north-east and bristle-leaved bent in the south-west.

Bilberry, ling, bracken, tormentil and sheep's-fescue – found on dry heathland

Ling/bell heather heath is found on slightly better soils than are stands of pure heather. It is often found on soils disturbed by such operations as gravel workings. Surveys indicate that the dry heaths of the New Forest account for some 6,000 hectares. However, within this predominantly heather area there are, where drainage is impeded, widespread areas of 'humid' heathland with ling, cross-leaved heath and purple moor-grass. To the south of the New Forest, Burton Common (an SSSI but not registered as Common Land) is a south-western type of dry heath where the heather is considerably older than that on any known New Forest site. The older plants are now degenerating and giving way to a luxuriant bryophyte and lichen flora in which young heather plants are colonising. The site provides a sharp ecological contrast with the heather communities in the nearby New Forest.

There is extensive heathland in the Western Weald (principally on the sandy, free-draining Folkestone and Sandgate Beds) which exhibits the characteristics of dry heathland vegetation. This includes Bramshott and Ludshott Commons and Woolmer Forest. The latter is regarded as being of national importance and is certainly the best remaining example of dry heath in the Western Weald.

On the tertiary deposits in the Thames Basin, Silchester Common has been notified as an SSSI because it is the best example in this area of dry ling heathland. On the coastal belt at Browndown, Gosport, an area owned by the Ministry of Defence provides extensive examples of dry heath, grassland heath and scrub heath. Browndown is important because it is the best example of dry heath, acid grassland and scrub developed on shingle in central southern England. It supports many rare or uncommon species and a wide range of ground-living lichens.

Humid Heathland occurs where the soils have impeded drainage and are in an intermediate state between wet and dry. Heather is relatively abundant and cross-leaved heath is to be found with purple moor-grass and a variety of associated vegetation depending on the nature of the site. Humid heathland is to be found in the New Forest in areas having a high water table and where gley podsols develop. These New Forest humid heaths are thought to be substantial (about 30 per cent of all New Forest heathlands) but they have not been acurately surveyed. Baddesley Common provides a further example in South Hampshire of 'humid' heath.

In the Western Weald examples of 'humid' heath are to be found at Blackmoor (which also contains extensive shallow pools rich in aquatic plants) and at Broxhead Common and Woolmer Forest. In the Thames Basin Hazeley Heath and Tadley and Yateley Commons exhibit 'humid' characteristics.

Wet Heathland occurs on sites where the drainage is impeded and the water table is within 10 centimetres of the surface for part of the year. Depending on the degree and permanence of the wetness the heather and cross-leaved heath may be accompanied by the dwarf gorses, purple moor-grass, heath grass, common tormentil, heath rush, cotton grass and sphagnum moss. Some of the rarer plants, like the sundews, marsh gentian, stags

horn club moss and marsh club moss are also to be found.

In the New Forest wet heaths and valley bogs, which develop on impermeable subsoils, cover about 2,833 hectares. If there is a high clay content in the underlying material, and the podzol which has formed is of a humus-gley type, heather, cross-leaved heath and purple moor-grass predominate. Heath grass, carnation sedge, common sedge, sundew, deer-grass and various species of sphagnum moss are also found in very wet areas.

Marsh violet, cotton grass, bogbean, tormentil and sedges – found on valley bogs.

Valley Bogs are wetter than, but continue to show certain characteristics of, wet heathland. They are found on sites where drainage is impeded and the water table is within 10 centimetres of the surface throughout the year. Peat accumulates in valleys and, when leached by water deficient in basic minerals, becomes increasingly acid and tolerable only to a few plants. These plants decompose slowly, release more acids and further deplete the nutritional value of the soil. Some biologically interesting valley bogs occur in the New Forest, supporting plants and animals not found in the cooler and wetter northern parts of Britain.

In the New Forest most of the bogs occur in the southern half of the area. For further information about New Forest and other valley bogs see the Rivers and Wetlands Topic Report.* In 1981 a field survey unit of the Nature Conservancy Council surveyed some 30 New Forest bogs, but the results of this study are not yet available. It is, however, known that depths of up to five feet of peat are common, and a depth of 20 feet has been recorded at Cranesmoor Bog.

The wildlife importance of valley bogs depends on the nutrient value of their soils and thus to the degree to which they have been enriched by groundwater carrying nutrients from more fertile surrounding land. It is important to retain the impoverished nature of remaining valley bogs; this necessitates care in the use of fertilisers, disposal of effluent, etc. in the surrounding catchment area. The plants chiefly characteristic of the more prevalent nutrient-poor valley bogs are purple moor-grass, bogbean, bog asphodel and cotton grass. Other frequent species, in addition to these found on wet heathland, are white beak-sedge, hare's tail cotton-grass, common sedge, marsh violet and deer grass.

Within the site of the Royal Aircraft Establishment at Farnborough there is an area of deep peat, not unlike a raised bog, on which there is an exceptionally rich acid bog flora. The site supports at least two hundred and fifty species of flowering plants and grasses. There are twelve species of orchid, some comparatively rare, and large populations of insect-feeding plants, e.g. common and pale butterwort, lesser bladderwort, common and long-leaved sundew as well as pale heath violet and yellow bartsia.

A further area with a rich bog-type flora, some of it rare, amid dry heath, conifer plantations and a complex of ponds and ditches is Bourley Water in the district of Hart.

Remaining areas of heathland on Shedfield and Wickham Commons and on the tertiary deposits between the chalk and the coastal belt, exhibit characteristics of wet, species-rich heathland. They provide examples of habitats poorly represented in this part of the county. Bog asphodel and sundews may still be found there.

Depending on the degree of nutrient richness and the rate at which water flows through the bog, various inter-related plant communities may develop. The most distinctive are the alder-carr woodlands and tussocks of sedge found along the main water-courses. Along slower moving tributary streams purple moor-grass is to be found, usually dominating the communities

Raft spider, heath spotted orchid and marsh gentian on moist, grassy heath

which include bog myrtle, black bog-rush, common reed, bog bean and marsh cinquefoil. On the bog itself may be found (depending on the nutrient content of the water and the wetness of the site) sphagnum mosses, cross-leaved heath, bog asphodel, sundews, white beak-sedge and cotton grass.

There are various transitional zones between these three basic types of plant community which also provide valuable wildlife habitats. For example, between the main water-courses and their tributaries, particularly where the central stream has cut into the subsoil, bog myrtle may form a distinctive zone, whilst on the bog the associated species include brown beak-sedge, pale butterwort, deer grass and stags-horn clubmoss.

Greatham Moor, to the west of Longmoor Camp, contains alder-carr woodland and bog where cranberry, bog asphodel, sundews, marsh violet, hare's-tail and bird's-foot are to be found. Silchester Common in the Thames Valley area also includes a small, but relatively rich, valley bog in which a central alder-carr is flanked by typical bog vegetation.

When the resulting peat is alkaline rather than acid, fen develops. Some sites, for example Conford Moor, a National Trust common near Passfield in the Western Weald, contain examples of both nutrient-rich fen and nutrient-poor bog vegetation which makes the site scientifically interesting.

Acid grassland is a type of vegetation containing many heathland species, found on dry, often nutrient-rich soils where, in some cases, fifty to sixty plant species may be found on one site. In some cases, particularly on the more fertile and well-drained sites, bracken may now be so dominant that it has obliterated the grasses and herbs. The main species found, in varying proportions, additional to those normally found on dry heaths are cross-leaved heath, moor mat grass, creeping bent and Yorkshire fog.

Acid grasslands, predominantly on clays and loams but occasionally on sands and gravels, account for some 4,452 hectares of the New Forest. Not all these evolved in the same way and some may still be in a transitional stage. This type of acid grassland, though usually dominated by bristle-leaved bent and purple moorgrass can be species rich in wetter areas, where marsh pennywort, lousewort and occasionally ivy-leaved bellflower can be found.

In the coastal belt dry heathland vegetation predominates on free draining soils and shingle. Most heaths are relics of former more extensive heathland and are now principally covered by gorse and grasses. However some sites still support other heathland species; principal among these sites are the Browndown Ranges at Stokes Bay, Gosport (an SSSI owned by the Ministry of Defence) and Sinah Common on Hayling Island, a golf course where areas of heathland have been conserved within the course.

Chalk Grassland* can occasionally support small scattered patches of heathland plants where acid clay immediately overlies the chalk. The patches are surrounded by typical chalk soils with their usual selection of chalkland plants. Those types of heath which occur on chalk have heather

Gorse (European and dwarf), ivy-leaved bellflower and creeping bent — found on acid grassland

and dwarf gorse mixed with typical chalkland vegetation, although upright brome tends to dominate these areas.

Examples of chalk heath are to be found at Farley Mount, a country park managed by Hampshire County Council and at Martin and Tidpit Downs, an SSSI in the western downlands of Hampshire. Martin Down is jointly owned by the Nature Conservancy Council and the County and District Councils. The value of Martin Down (249 hectares), which supports an exceptionally rich chalkland flora and a rich invertebrate fauna, is enhanced by small patches of chalk heath which provide the best example in Britain of this phenomena. Martin Down is well documented and provides an opportunity for studying the effects of management on wildlife.

Scrub occurs where heathland is in the process of reverting to woodland. It may contain, in addition to the remnants of former heathland vegetation, bramble, broom, sweet vernal grass, various bent grasses and oak, birch and pine trees.

Many heaths would now be better described as 'scrub with heath'. These include, in the coastal belt, Butlock's Heath and Hamble Common; in the Western Weald, Kingsley and Short Heath Commons and, in the Thames Basin, Newtown and Burghclere Commons and parts of Yateley Common and Bourley Water.

In addition to the transitional scrub type of habitats, many heathlands exhibit the characteristics of a number of other types of heathland vegetation. For example at Hazeley Heath, where a ridge of Bracklesham Sands is capped by plateau gravel, there is a wide range of plant communities including examples of dry heathland, wet heathland bog, acid grassland and scrub heath. The heath has been modified by fire and the subsequent domination by purple moor-grass. Birch colonisation is widespread. The common rights of grazing and estovers which still exist are insufficiently exercised to control the latter. Nevertheless Hazeley Heath has been notified as an SSSI, not because of any unique features but because it comprises a relatively large tract of varied heathland habitat which is now becoming nationally scarce.

Heathland Animals

Those species of vertebrates which largely depend on heathland for their survival in Hampshire, and which are now becoming rare due to its decline, are the Dartford warbler, stonechat, sand lizard, smooth snake and natterjack toad. Burton Common supports populations of sand lizard and smooth snakes and they have also been recorded in recent years at Broxhead Common. Woolmer Pond continues to support a population of natterjack toads.

Many species alternate between heathland and another habitat. Curiously few species share heathland with deciduous woodlands. Those that do include the adder (which still sometimes undertakes a short annual migration between dry overwintering sites and damper summer feeding grounds) chaffinch, wood lark and the wren, which likes both high heather and close canopy woodland. The common lizard is widespread and shares heathland with a variety of habitats.

Adder amongst bracken

The tree pipit and grasshopper warbler live both on heathland and in young plantations. Redshank, lapwing, snipe and curlew live on heath or wetland. Species sharing heathland with chalk grassland include the skylark and meadow pipit.

Lowland heaths are important hunting grounds for several species of predatory birds and some mammals. Of the birds, the buzzard, sparrow hawk, kestrel and hobby hunt widely in the breeding season. The hobby, in particular, is found on the lowland heaths and chalk grasslands of Hampshire, Wiltshire, Sussex and Surrey, and seeks out breeding sites in isolated tree clumps. In winter, merlins, hen harriers and great grey shrike also hunt in heathland for food. The nightjar is associated with dry, sandy heath with scattered trees but being active at twilight or night-time is difficult to locate.

Species restricted to habitats like heathland tend to be subject to periodic, drastic declines. They are especially vulnerable to severe winter weather. If their habitats are destroyed they would be unable to recover. Thus in the New Forest the Dartford warbler population dropped from some 380 breeding pairs in 1961 to only two in 1966 after successive severe winters, but by 1974 the number of breeding pairs had recovered and stood at around 240. In 1978, when the last credible survey was carried out, there was estimated to be only 118 pairs, yet in 1982 there were thought to be some 150 to 200 pairs. Similarly the stonechat population

of the New Forest fell from 430 pairs to 58 between 1961 and 1963; again the numbers had recovered to about 350 pairs by 1974. In 1978 the number of pairs was probably in the region of 300 but the 1981/82 winter is thought to have reduced this number to less than 120 pairs in 1982. The wood lark's range has retreated southwards and now probably only some 200 pairs breed in Britain. One quarter of these are estimated to be in the New Forest. In the same way the breeding range of the red-backed shrike has retracted considerably this century and although a breeding population of these birds remained in the New Forest even this was halved in the early to mid 1960s and this bird is now virtually extinct there. The last record of the red-backed shrike breeding at Tadley Common was 1969.

The sand lizard, formerly found, though not in abundance, over the heathlands of Hampshire, Dorset, Surrey and Sussex, now only exists in one colony in Hampshire. It is thought to be extinct in the New Forest; much of the area is too wet, and that which is not has been over-enthusiastically burnt.

What is to be found on any particular site depends on the extent of the heathland, its condition, the extent of colonisation by trees and shrubs, the extent of burning and the nature of the surrounding areas. For example Yateley Common, (now largely covered with gorse, birch and scots pine, but which still contains large

Emperor moth, silver-studded blue and grayling butterflies on heathland.

areas of dry heath and acid grassland) supports many characteristic birds of heathlands; for example, wood lark, stonechat, nightjar, Dartford warbler and hobby.

Heathland Insects and Spiders

Heathland supports a limited range of insects and invertebrates which are dependant, or are increasingly becoming dependant, on remaining heathland habitats. The New Forest, because of the variety of habitats it contains and their close juxtaposition, is especially important for the rarer species.

Heathland habitats are important for the predatory groups they support: these include dragonflies, spiders, ants and solitary wasps. Dragonflies breed in ponds and streams on the wetter parts and feed on the open heath or on woodland edges. They are able to travel up to fifteen kilometres in search of their prey — numerous heathland insects. Most common are the golden-ringed dragonfly, four-spotted libellula and the common sympetrum. In certain parts of the New Forest it is still possible to find colonies of the rarer damselflies (*Ischurna pumilio* and *Ceriagrion tenellum*) though these have been severely reduced in numbers through the drainage and reclamation, or pollution, of their clean water habitats elsewhere.

Spiders characteristic of heathlands are wolf spiders and crab spiders. Wolf spiders, many species of which are widespread, do not trap their prey in a web but actively hunt it. The pink crab spider (*Thomisus onustus*) lurks in flower heads, especially the cross-leaved heath, waiting to seize suitable insects as they collect the nectar.

The sandy, well-drained soils of acid heaths like the New Forest and Wealdon Heaths support large colonies of ants. *Lasius alienus* and *Tetramorium caespitum* are particularly found on dry heath, *Lasius flavus* and *Myrmica sabuleti* on grassy heath and *Formica fusca* and *Myrmica ruginodis* on areas of scrub.

Some of the ant colonies occupy and defend territories of many square metres. To avoid the drying winds of spring and the heat of summer and occasional heath fires, their nests can extend to as much as one metre below the soils surface. Velvet ants, *Mutilla europaea* actually a wasp but so called because the females are wingless, are also to be found.

Sandy soils also support the sand wasp which preys on large caterpillars, paralyses them and drags them into nests in the ground which are then sealed. The female wasp lays her eggs on the prey so that the wasp grub can commence its life with an adequate supply of food. Other wasps, like the potter wasp, skim low over the ground in search of spiders. Their nests are made of clay, are flask-shaped and are attached to heather stems.

Grasshoppers (mainly the common green and mottled) like dry grassy and bare areas of heathland as do ground-hoppers which overwinter on heath as nymphs. The rarer heath grasshopper is now only found in localised areas on certain Dorset and Hampshire heaths. Various bugs and beetles make their home on heathland including the heath assassin bug and the green tiger beetle. The latter are strong-flying carnivorous insects with (for their size) large eyes and large jaws. They like sandy soils for their larva to burrow in.

Heathland is not so rich as chalk grassland in butterflies and moths, although both day and night-flying species are included. The most common moths are the Emperor moth, the narrow-winged pug, the common heath moth and the fox moth. Butterflies characteristic of heathland include the silver-studded blue, green hairstreak, grayling and small heath. Woolmer Forest and the Royal Aircraft Establishment site at Farnborough support, respectively, thirty-four and thirty-six species. Tadley Common, a mixture of wet and dry heath, supports twenty-three species.

*Rivers and Wetlands: Hampshire County Planning Department, 1983.

*Chalk Grassland: Hampshire County Planning Department, 1983

Cattle grazing New Forest heathland.

The Care of Hampshire's Heathlands

Simply retaining heathland is not sufficient to ensure the maintenance of the Heather plant. Its life-span, like that of the woodland coppice*, can be prolonged. If it is continually cut, grazed or burnt, the root-stock may regenerate many times. Heathland is generally managed on the assumption that it will, during the course of approximately 25 to 30 years, pass through a series of stages — the pioneer, building, mature and degenerate stages.

The pioneer phase is associated with regeneration from seed. This usually takes six years and is when the plant is becoming established and putting on some early growth. Regeneration from seed is relatively uncommon and the seedlings often suffer from drought during the summer. With post burn root-stock regeneration the heathland passed straight to the building phase (up to about 10 years) when there is production of maximum cover and density of canopy.

The mature phase (up to about 20 or 25 years) is when the production of shoots and flowers slows down and the central frame branches spread and admit light to the ground. Finally, the plant reaches a degenerate phase (from about 25 years onwards) when death of the main branches occurs and wide gaps appear and become occupied by other species.

The sequence of development may be controlled by management, but when management ceases, or the ling so degenerates that the re-establishment of young plants becomes difficult, different types of vegetation appear. A simplified and tentative relationship between vegetation and management for Hampshire's heathland is indicated in the diagram on page 18.

Where, outside the New Forest, heathland is now managed it is only exceptionally that it is managed for traditional purposes. It may have been acquired for management as a nature reserve or to maintain it as an example of a semi-natural habitat. More likely, it will have been acquired for a different purpose and it is fortuitous that this use has allowed the heathland to survive. This applies in the case of those extensive areas of heathland acquired by the Ministry of Defence.

The larger areas of heathland in Hampshire are, as indicated in Appendix Two, generally either managed or owned by the Forestry Commission, the Property Services Agency, the County Council and the National Trust. Their future seems assured.

The Forestry Commission, acting on behalf of the Ministry of Agriculture, Fisheries & Food and the Crown, owns and manages extensive areas of heathland, principally in the New Forest. There the Crown area extends to over 27,000 hectares of which there are 18,500 hectares of open forest waste. Within this area of open forest waste there are 14,100 hectares of heathland and valley bog.* Elsewhere the Forestry Commission owns and manages remnants of former heathlands in Alice Holt Forest, Ringwood Forest, the Forest of Bere (at Ridge Copse and on the eastern edge of West Walk) and at Bramshill.

The Property Services Agency (PSA) manages Woolmer Forest on behalf of the Ministry of Defence. Large areas of heathland remain within the firing ranges, tank-training grounds and ancillary areas. The PSA is assisted in its management by the Conservation Officer of the Ministry of Defence. A large measure of success in conserving wildlife on the remaining areas of heathland has been achieved. By using volunteers the Conservation Officer has compiled extensive lists of, and information about, the wildlife of Woolmer Forest; the lists include many rare species. The protection of these species alone is a good reason for safeguarding these habitats. Similar inventories are being prepared for all MOD sites which, in this area, include parts of Bramshott and Ludshott Commons.

The County Council, because of its country parks, picnic areas and local nature reserves, retains a considerable interest in heathland. The largest area under County Council management is Yateley Common near Camberley, which is principally managed as a country park. At East Headley the County Council leases and manages Broxhead Common as a heathland local nature reserve.

The Hampshire & Isle of Wight Naturalists' Trust owns and manages a number of nature reserves, some containing heathland; for example, Brockenhurst Woods in the New Forest, where there are some 28 hectares of good quality wet and dry heaths.

The National Trust owns and manages the greater part of Ludshott Common near Liphook, and also parts of Conford Moor and Passfield Common between Whitehill and Liphook. All these are remains of once more-extensive heathland.

Because of the legal difficulties of removing rights of common, many of smaller remnants of heathland have survived. However many of these relict sites, because of the economics of dealing with small unproductive areas, present severe management problems which, if not resolved, will soon result in their loss as heathland habitats.

Where heathlands are not registered commons, agricultural reclamation and afforestation can pose a threat, as can encroaching development in the form of houses, roads, mineral extraction and military activities. Where heathlands are registered commons the rights of common, albeit now largely unexercised, coupled with the poor nutrient value of most heathland soils, have prevented agricultural and silvicultural improvements. The difficulties of enclosure have also impeded the rate of urban encroachment. However, a recent development causing concern is the number of proceedings to remove common land from the registers. The grounds for these actions are often very technical, and sometimes the actions are incontestable by the registration authorities. Action by Parliament is required to curtail this development.

It is the small relict heathlands which mainly require care and protection. This section of the booklet concentrates on these areas although some of the comments apply equally to the larger heathlands. Suggestions are made on how the problems facing the small relic heathlands might be overcome.

Current Problems

The greatest single problem facing heathland is neglect. The problem is greatest for the small, scattered remnants of previously extensive heathland. The causes of neglect are many but the main ones are:—

Stonechat on gorse, bristle-leaved bent and broom.

Lack of a place for heathland in the local agricultural economy of the twentieth century lowland;

lack of knowledge about the nature conservation value of the heathland habitat;

the importance of size when considering the practicability of retaining the remaining areas of heathland; and

failure to prevent the enrichment of heathland soils.

Hampshire's heathland, largely an anachronism, survives in an intensively-farmed and developed lowland county. Only in the New Forest does the mixture of heathland, acid grassland, valley bog and unenclosed deciduous woodland still maintain the economy of a pastoral regime rooted in a former social and economic system. Few of the three to four hundred commoners who still exercise their rights over the New Forest, to graze cattle and ponies and turn pigs out in the pannage season to forage for 'mast' (acorns and beech-mast) are now dependent on these rights. Those which are, maintain their standards of living by turning out more animals. This practice causes overgrazing, the consequences of which may be a deterioration of the biological diversity of the Forest. Evidence[13] now available suggests that grassland, which thrives on grazing, is expanding at the expense of heathland which is more susceptible to being overgrazed. In 1977 the Nature Conservancy Council commissioned an investigation by the University of Southampton, under the supervision of Dr. Rory Putnam and Dr. Peter Edwards, into the food and feeding behaviour of cattle and ponies in the New Forest, the productivity and nutrient status of the vegetation and the effects of grazing on the habitat. The conclusions of this investigation, now being considered by the Nature Conservancy Council, are likely to be of considerable importance in the long-term management of the New Forest's heathland.

There is much ignorance about the value of heathland as a wildlife habitat. The situation should soon be much improved under the provisions of the Wildlife and Countryside Act 1981, both the owners of the more important sites, (the SSSIs) and the local planning authorities are to be notified by the Nature Conservancy Council of the value of heathland habitats for wildlife conservation and of the actions or operations which would detrimentally affect these areas. The prospect of a loss of heathland caused by such actions has thereby been reduced. Although some owners will invoke the provisions for compensation through management agreements, and thus some areas will be saved, on sites where SSSIs have not been notified it will be possible for others to persist and diminish, or destroy, heathland habitats. Fortunately in the case of heathland, direct threats from agriculture and similar operations are not generally as great as those from other sources. The greater threats arise from unsuitable management; overuse by the public bringing problems of trampling, erosion or fire, while too little use can allow invasion by scrub and trees.

The third main cause of neglect is the size of the site. Size is important for the maintenance of diversity within heathland. Many species of animals, especially birds, require large territories. A large site is generally more robust; it can survive temporary encroachment, overuse and unintentional fires. There is much more chance of retaining a range of pioneer, building, mature and degenerate heather if the site is large.

The semi-natural vegetation of heathland was formerly stabilised by grazing and burning. Heaths can seldom be maintained without periodic intervention by man, although many persist for years without visible signs of reversion to woodland. However, a policy of non-intervention seldom maintains heathland. About twenty-five or more years after the cessation of grazing, cutting, burning, turf cutting or bracken gathering the heather ages, and if near to a seed source of potentially colonising trees and plants the area becomes scrub and woodland.

Grazing by commoners' stock is now seldom practised, outside the New Forest, nor is the cutting of turf and peat for fuel or any other of the one-time important common rights. In recent years almost the only activities that have been operating to prevent tree growth have been rabbit grazing (severely reduced by myxomatosis), accidental fires, and public pressure for conservation management by volunteers. In north Hampshire considerable areas that were heathland at the turn of the century are now birch woodland.

Where heathland does remain in large blocks in public ownership administered by such bodies as the Property Services Agency or the Forestry Commission, the problems presented for the long-term safeguarding of the habitat are few and relatively straightforward. This is not the case with scattered, unfenced and fragmented remains of former heathland, not in public or other secure ownership. These small sites have a greater length of edge per unit than larger ones and consequently are affected more by fertiliser drift and invasion by non-heath species. The management options they offer are generally fewer and the effect of an accidental fire or natural disaster may be more damaging.

Cutting and burning controls the pattern of woodland/heathland/acid grassland.

Fairy cakes and Grisettes — fungi that can be found on heathland

Provided that these small scattered remnants of former heathland still exhibit sufficient characteristics to warrant future management as heathland, then it is worth acting to secure this management. Even when sites are now so overrun by scrub and trees that reversion to heathland may be impractical, they may still be used for public enjoyment, visual amenity or timber production.

Even when the value of the heathland habitat, whether extensive or restricted, is appreciated there are often severe management problems, particularly to ensure the balance of nutrients. It is important to understand that:

(a) the food requirements of heathland plants are low;
(b) any process, whether natural or artificial, leading to increased food levels will result in vegetational change;
(c) it is easier to raise the food level of heathland soils, often unsuspectingly by infiltration of the groundwater, than it is to remove nutrients from the area; and
(d) natural progression of vegetation change, such as increase in gorse, birch, bracken or purple moorgrass, can raise food levels in upper soil horizons by reducing the amount of leaching. This makes it difficult to change the vegetation back to some previous stage in the progression.

The ways by which nutrients enter heathland, and their effect, need more research. Two ways are the drift of fertilisers and the flow of drainage from adjacent land. Whilst it may be possible to minimise the enrichment, the best solution is an adequate size of site, especially where agricultural reclamation is taking place on surrounding land. The effects of nutrient additions are significant in the case of dry heathland but are particularly so in the case of wet heathland. Here it is especially important that protection is given to a sufficiently large area. Under some conditions there may be a natural accumulation of plant nutrients in the upper parts of the soil. This occurs under stands of gorse, bracken and birch and it makes the re-establishment of certain types of heather difficult, or sometimes impossible.

Because of the importance of maintaining low levels of plant foods in soils, it is essential to consider both the inputs and losses of nutrients from a particular area. Losses occur when heather is burnt as a form of management. Chapman[14] showed that, except for nitrogen and phosphorus, losses incurred during burning could be replenished by inputs from rainfall over a twelve-year period. Dr. Chapman is currently undertaking work to see if the levels of phosphorus can be maintained by atmospheric inputs. Gorse normally maintains soil nitrogen levels and can sometimes cause an increase, so any additional nitrogen in the soil water arising from run-off drift from adjoining farmland would prove excessive for most heathland sites.

What Can be Done to Conserve Heathlands

To help overcome the problems arising from the neglect of heathlands various actions can be taken by those concerned.

What the County Council Can Do

The County Council is concerned about the value of heathlands from wildlife, historic, scenic and recreational points of view and the need to protect and manage remaining areas of it. The County Council will:—

Draw attention to the value of heathland. This booklet, and the development of the Countryside Heritage Policy, will help to draw attention to the nature conservation value of the heathland habitat.

Continue to manage the areas of heathland for which it is responsible in a manner which conserves wildlife whilst providing facilities for informal countryside recreation.

Assist owners and managers of heathland, by advice on what needs to be done in particular instances, or by obtaining more specialist advice when this is required.

The County Council will give practical help either directly or by seeking assistance from volunteers. The County Council and Countryside Commission are encouraging the British Trust for Conservation Volunteers to set up further groups of conservation volunteers in Hampshire through the appointment of Hampshire organiser based in Winchester. Grant aid for heathland management can also be made available, in appropriate instances, from the County Council's Environmental Improvement Fund.

What the Landowner Can Do

Owners, managers and, where still applicable, commoners exercising rights over heathland, should:—

Consider the wildlife, historic and scenic value of those heathlands and how, through their management decisions, the heath might be sustained or even improved.

Seek help and advice from those individuals and organisations with specialist knowledge of managing heathland habitats. The use of volunteer labour to undertake otherwise uneconomic tasks of conserving heathland, e.g. pulling out young trees and clearing scrub, is particularly relevant.

What the Public Can Do

There is a number of things that you, the reader, can do to help conserve areas of heathland, especially the small, scattered remains which are to be found in Hampshire.

Record the wildlife. This can be an interesting and rewarding exercise to those visiting the countryside provided that they adhere to the Countryside Code and seek the consent of landowners to enter private land. These records may be of subsequent use to the land-owners and managers of that heathland, or to authorities giving advice, for their records might help in making the right decisions about conservation of the wildlife or archaeological features concerned.

Adopt an area of heathland. This may help to 'warden' it and, hopefully, to prevent accidental fires, encroach-ment by unauthorised development and unlawful enclosure.

Organise volunteeer labour. Control of unwanted vegeta-tion and scrub, removal of rubbish, the cutting of fire-breaks and control of cars and visitors, by volunteers, can help create conditions favourable to certain species dependent on heathland. Volunteer labour must be properly supervised and the operations carried out in a professional way at an appropriate time of the year.

A considerable amount of advice and guidance on the management of heathlands is available and the more important sources of information and advice are set out below.

Sources of Information and Advice

Further advice and assistance can, in the first instance, be obtained by writing to:
The County Planning Officer,
The Castle, Winchester, SO23 8UE.

by telephoning:
The Countryside Section of the Planning Department, Telephone 54411 (Extension 654).

Other sources are:—
The Assistant Regional Officer (South),
The Nature Conservancy Council,
Shrubbs Hill Road,
Lyndhurst, SO4 7DJ — Telephone Lyndhurst 2840

The Conservation Officer,
The Hampshire & Isle of Wight Naturalists' Trust Ltd.,
8 Market Place,
Romsey, SO5 8NB — Telephone Romsey 513786

The Secretary,
The Farming & Wildlife Advisory Group,
c/o Ministry of Agriculture Fisheries and Food,
Cromwell House,
Andover Road,
Winchester, SO23 7EN — Telephone Winchester 63500

The Hampshire Organiser,
The British Trust for Conservation Volunteers,
c/o County Recreation Department,
North Hill Close,
Andover Road,
Winchester, SO22 6AQ — Telephone Winchester 64221

---

*Coppice is a system of woodland management whereby trees are regularly cut, near to the ground, to provide a renewable supply of small wood and fuel.

*The figure of 14,100 hectares has been obtained from the Forestry Commission's management records. Its estimate of heathland within the New Forest, is taken from A Nature Conservation Review, by S.A. Ratcliffe for the Natural Environ-ment Research Council and the Nature Conservancy Council, Cambridge University Press, 1977. Here the figure is 14,370 hectares.

Appendix One

Management Techniques

There are two principal management approaches: protective management and species management.

Protective management is generally more applicable to small, scattered, threatened sites, whilst species management is more appropriate to the larger blocks. However, there are likely to be occasions when the techniques outlined under one heading apply equally to the other.

Objectives:

Ideally, the objectives of management should be directed towards maintaining and improving the value of the site as a wildlife habitat whilst being realistic about the problems of so doing. In practice this means that few sites can be burnt or grazed; that attention must be paid to the requirements for informal recreation (heaths are important visual amenities and open spaces for the public at large), and that the owner's requirements should be borne in mind.

Because the objectives and criteria will vary from site to site it is impracticable to prescribe treatment for individual sites in a booklet like this. Nevertheless, there is little doubt that on large sites where burning or grazing could be introduced, or improved, the establishment of a heather/grass mosaic would come nearest to providing an acceptable compromise.

Whichever type of management is dictated by the site characteristics, land tenure and other factors, the first essential is to set out the objectives of management in a management plan, however brief. This must attempt to achieve a balance between the short and long-term interests of those concerned, yet secure the survival of the site as heathland with all that this implies for the plants and animals associated with it.

A management plan must be flexible enough to take account of unforeseen events such as drought, accidental fire, new information which may become available and changes in management techniques. Where there are groups of sites the specific priorities for an individual one should be decided in relation to the overall plan for the group.

A management plan is not an end in itself; it must be implemented. Its effectiveness must be monitored and the plan reviewed to see if it is lacking in any way.

Protective Management

Protective management of heathland is designed principally to prevent or reduce known adverse or damaging effects. It includes the control of scrub and other invasive vegetation, prevention of fires and the control of vehicles and people. In some areas litter and refuse may also be problems requiring attention.

The loss of heathland by invasion of other plant species can also occur as a result of either too much, or too little, deliberate burning. Changes brought about by invasive species can be rapid after fire. Four species create the greatest problems.

Birch and Pine Where these have become established, control by burning will not be adequate. Once birch seedlings have reached a certain size burning may even encourage their spread. The balance between birch, pine and heather is a delicate one. Too little, or too much burning has a detrimental effect on grazing and can shift the balance in favour of birch and pine. Both species can be controlled by cutting but birch will also require the treatment of the remaining stumps with a suitable herbicide. When the trees are young, they may be pulled or treated with a local application of a herbicide such as 'Roundup'. However, birch supports a number of insects and this should be borne in mind before removing all of it.

Bracken This colonises more readily than heather where there are repeated fires. It tends to enrich the soil by bringing up nutrients and creating a mull (brown forest soil) type humus. A spread of bracken is a serious problem on heathland sites. The traditional means of control is by cutting or crushing, but where bracken is invading *Calluna* heathland this is often inefficient and could have a deleterious effect upon the heather. With the advent of 'Asulam', a selective herbicide, a more effective means of control became available. 'Asulam' is a herbicide with low toxicity which has little effect upon most plants, but does kill bracken and ferns and can scorch young trees. Bracken is however an important plant in the landscape and forms some interesting associations with other plants; for example the wild gladiolus is now found in Britain only amongst bracken on wood edges in Hampshire.

Rose Bay Willow Herb This is not a serious problem on many heaths but it is becoming more abundant in some parts of the county. When present in relatively low numbers it should be removed before it seeds, by pulling, to reduce its spread and thus avoid a more serious problem.

Common gorse This is an important component of heathland communities, particularly as it provides the habitat for the Dartford warbler and is rich in insects and spiders. In some cases, however, it may be necessary to give priority to the heather and control or reduce the amount of gorse. Grazing is the most effective means. Burning generally results in both regeneration from roots and abundant germination from seeds. Cutting or swiping also results in regeneration. Cutting followed by herbicide application to the stumps is probably the most satisfactory way to reduce the amount of gorse on a site. Cutting followed by periodic swiping is suitable especially if grassland conditions are required. The eradication of gorse is likely to be a lengthy procedure since seed will remain in the soil for a considerable time following the removal of the parent plants.

21

Sites without protection can be subject to accidental fires, and as a consequence contain few older stands of heather. Protection from fire makes formal management much easier. Firebreaks are necessary for the protection not only of wildlife habitats, but also adjoining properties. They can provide a habitat in themselves for plants and animals that require open sandy conditions. A ploughed firebreak can be effective but is often conspicuous. It does, however, provide an additional habitat so the time of year when firebreaks are ploughed can affect the wild-life in this area. A mown firebreak is less conspicuous but is also less effective in stopping a fire. However, it can be incorporated as part of the management pro-gramme to maintain areas of lower and younger heather, and their associated animal communities. Firebreaks can be used as access routes to different parts of a reserve.

In addition to a system of firebreaks an adequate water supply is needed. If natural pools are not available it may be necessary to provide water tanks or install artificial pools that will not empty as the water table drops in summer. Fire-beaters should also be provided in stands at suitable locations; rendezvous points and fire pens should be arranged after meeting with the local fire brigade, Forestry Commission representatives and other organisations. It is desirable in high-risk areas to arrange annual briefings with the local fire brigade to familiarise its officers with such matters as entry points, usable tanks, sources of water supply, etc.

Heathland is sensitive to damage by trampling, and soil erosion can become a serious problem once the vegeta-tion cover is lost. Because the greater part of the nutrient fund of the heathland plant/soil system is contained in the surface layer of the soil, restoration of eroded sites can become a long and difficult process.

Species Management

A number of heathland plants and animals, whilst not necessarily rare, are more demanding in their ecological requirements than the more abundant species. In some cases changes in land use, or simply loss of habitat, leads to a reduction in the numbers of plants and animals. As a result more specific management may be needed to ensure their survival.

Since different species of plants and animals have different growing, maturing and reproduction require-ments, it is not surprising that conflicts can arise when relatively small and isolated areas have to be managed for a number of different species. Where individual sites, or groups of sites, are of sufficient size, many of these conflicts can be resolved. With small sites there is always the possibility that, even with careful manage-ment, one may lose the individual species or a particular type of habitat, e.g. where marsh gentian is in active competition with heather which requires periodic burn-ing. The best management procedure for one may not be compatible with the requirements of the other, and in some cases neither may be ideal when considering the long-term survival of heathland at a particular site. One example relates to the sand lizard, which prefers old heather and its structural diversity. Such areas can be maintained if trees are removed as they appear, but an accidental fire, a severe winter, an attack by heather beetle or a drought may produce conditions where sub-

sequent regeneration of the heather will be slow, difficult or even impossible.

The problem is less important on larger, more diverse areas, where sufficient ground allows the development of a mosaic of different-aged heather and a range of associated plants. Such a mosaic reduces the risk of fires spreading, allows re-colonisation of newly burnt areas from adjacent 'reservoirs' and also reduces the time required for the redevelopment of older stands.

Burning, Mowing, Cutting, Hoeing and Grazing

Various management techniques may be used for both protective management and species management where sufficient *Calluna* heath remains.

Burning: A programme of heather burning should only be carried out as part of a long-term plan designed to build a mosaic of different age stands of heather. Some areas should be kept free from fire. In general, an interval of 15 to 20 years between burns is reasonable. Burning more frequently leads to under-representation of old stands of heather and their associated flora and fauna. It can also favour the spread of 'less desirable' species such as bracken, birch and gorse, the latter especially where the soil has been disturbed. Burning frequently may lead to difficulties in root stock regenera-tion and problems of scrub invasion.

If fires are too fierce the surface humus is set alight and heather seeds lying on the surface are destroyed. The replacement of old plants by seedlings is not very common.[15] Where the heather is extremely old regenera-tion after fire takes many years but, because of the rarity of old stands, relatively little is known about their regenerative capabilities. However, if heather does not regenerate quickly enough, other species may take its place and, eventually, suppress it altogether.

It is therefore desirable to ensure that the conditions under which heather is burnt are those under which it will most frequently regenerate. This depends to a large extent on individual site conditions, but heather will regenerate most rapidly after burning when it is in the 'building' phase because:

(a) the plant community is still vigorous;
(b) other plants have been suppressed;
(c) the amount of dry material on the surface is not so thick that it creates too much heat;
(d) the condition of the surface humus is conducive to successful germination of the heather seed where necessary to supplement regeneration from the root stalk.

The season during which heather or heathland vegetation may be burned without a permit from the Ministry of Agriculture, Fisheries and Food extends from 1 October to 31 March. Experience has shown that satisfactory burning in autumn is difficult, because either it is too windy for safe burning or the vegetation is too wet. The most satisfactory months are February and March. Even then care must be exercised, as seen from this extract from Gilbert White's letters.[16]

"Yet about March or April according to the dryness of the season, such vast heath-fires are lighted up that they often get to a masterless head and catching the hedges have sometimes been communicated to the underwoods, wood and coppices where great damage has ensued. The plea for those burning is that when the old coat of heath etc. is consumed, young will sprout up and afford much tender browse for cattle, but where there is large old firs, one fire, following the roots, consumes the very ground; so that for hundreds of acres nothing is to be seen but smoulder and desolation. The whole circuit round looking like the cinders of a volcano".

To avoid such hazards, correct procedures must be followed and enough experienced field staff be available. The size of the area to be burnt, and the duration of burning, must be carefully planned and will depend on the planned rotation, local conditions, available labour, time available for burning, etc. As a general rule, not more than one hectare of lowland heath should be burnt at a time. Further hints are:

(a) always to burn against the wind, so as to control the fire and ensure it is hot enough for a good clean burn, but not so hot that it does damage;

(b) not to burn on stony ground, steep slopes or thin soils when very dry. This is to avoid roots being killed and to prevent frost damage if the following winter is severe;

(c) not to burn peat areas when very dry as the peat may ignite and destroy the heather roots;

(d) to select and mark the areas to be burnt well in advance of the burning season;

(e) to inform owners of adjoining land, especially woodland, when it is planned to burn.

Mowing and cutting: In many areas burning is not convenient or even possible. This may be due to the proximity of forestry or houses, restrictions imposed by the terms of a lease, a lack of suitably experienced assistance or because of adverse public reaction. In such cases cutting or mowing can be considered as an alternative form of heathland management.

The greatest danger associated with cutting heather is that there may be an adverse effect upon older and degenerate stands. In dry summers, old heather may not regenerate from the roots as young stands do. Advantages of cutting are that it can be carried out almost regardless of the weather, and is far less labour-intensive. It is suggested that heather cutting should be restricted to the same season as that allowed for burning (1 October to 31 March). To promote regeneration it is essential that the cut material is removed from the site. This is easy to do as the heather is cut close to the ground and can be raked up or baled. In the New Forest, baled heather is often used in road foundations.

Preliminary studies suggest that mowing and baling is a useful substitute for heather burning but on humid sites in the New Forest purple moor-grass tends to dominate afterwards. Cutting and subsequent carting away of the heather removes more nutrients from the site than burning. Also, older stands of heather are easily damaged by vehicles and their passage should therefore be kept to a minimum. The use of a swipe, with its tendency to fragment the cut material, is best restricted to maintaining mown fire-breaks and similar areas. It should be carried out as a regular 'topping', so that large amounts of cut material are not returned to the soil at any one time. Examples of this form of heather management can be seen on Blackmoor Golf Course and the Longmoor Rifle Range in East Hampshire.

Hoeing: Hoeing using a rotary tiller is a rejuvenating technique which enables heathland to replenish itself within 2 to 3 years. Mattocking (a type of hand hoeing) can have the same effect.

Grazing: To graze a heath satisfactorily requires very careful planning to match numbers of stock with the availability of food. Although the productivity of many heaths could be improved by creating fescue and bent grass pastures but they would not then have any value as heathland. Managed heather, ten or more years old, can support 2.5 sheep a hectare whilst still maintaining the heathland habitat. Higher stocking rates of five sheep a hectare are possible but will encourage the establishment of grasses at the expense of heather because grasses withstand heavy grazing better than heather. Cattle can replace sheep at the rate of one cow per five sheep. Although grazing is one of the best ways to sustain heathland, little if any grazing of heathland now occurs outside the New Forest. Here densities of less than one cow for one to two hectares, one deer for three to four hectares or one pony for five to seven hectares are considered to permit regeneration of the heather.[17] Sheep 'browse' rather than graze the young, palatable and nutritious leading shoots of ling especially in winter and early spring. Cattle rarely eat shoots. Further information on this subject can be found in a recent study commissioned by the Nature Conservancy Council.*

The feeding value of ling is highest up to its fourth year, after which the quality declines, but this is compensated for by an increase in the quantity up to about seven years. Thereafter there is a general decline in the feeding value.

Although managed heather can live almost indefinitely, an unmanaged area of heath has a life span of about 20 to 25 years. Ideally, from a grazing point of view, it should not be allowed to go too far into the 'mature' phase (say to fifteen years) after burning. The rotation adopted for burning, cutting or otherwise controlling heather should therefore be based on treating one-fifteenth of the ling acreage in any one year.

Heather cannot survive if continuously close-grazed. However, most heathland contains a variety of vegetation allowing sheep and cattle to turn to associated grasses, e.g. purple moor-grass, moor mat grass, bristle-leaved bent, wavy hair grass, sheep's fescue and sweet vernal grass, from the early summer onwards. The least palatable grasses like bristle-leaved bent are not eaten until late October or November when the more palatable grasses have disappeared. Grasses tolerate, and even thrive on, close grazing but this may suppress other heathland plants like tormentil and bedstraw.

Bracken, rarely eaten by sheep, provides ponies with an alternative source of herbage during the late summer when the plant is mature and the fronds open. It is toxic and some deaths occur each year in the New Forest when eaten in excess. Young bracken shoots also, are carcinogenic. In winter, New Forest ponies eat large quantities of gorse and holly and many animals would not survive some winters without these shrubs.

*Putman, Edwards, Ellis and Pratt of Southampton University, on 'Food and Feeding Behaviour of Cattle and Ponies in the New Forest' (1982).

2.   Cross-leaved Heath

3.   Sand Lizard (male)

4.   Silver-studded Blue butterfly

5.   European Gorse

6.   Ling and Bell Heather

7.   Bell Heather and Purple Moor-grass & Bristle Bent

Appendix Two

Heathland in Hampshire

(handwritten margin notes:)
Crains moor Common
Embley wood
Pennington Common
Kingston North ?

Name	O.S. Grid Reference	Area (ha)	Status	Dry	Wet	Humid	Acid Grass	Valley Bog	Scrub
South Hampshire and the New Forest Area									
Baddesley Common	393215	37	SSSI	•		•	•		•
Badminston Common Fields Heath	455020	30	SSSI	•	•	•	•		•
Browndown	580990	64.6	SSSI	•			•		•
Burton	195955	40.5	SSSI	•			•		•
Chark Common	575023	41	Common	•			•		•
Cranemoor	207949	15.5	SSSI, Common	•			•		
Hamble	480061	23	FC, NT	•	•	•	•		•
New Forest area	298081	14370	Common	•	•	•	•		•
Shedfield Common	563130	13	Common				•		
Shelley Common	315190	25							•
Sinah Common	695993	10		•					•
Wickham	588108	27	Common			•	•		
Thames Basin									
Bartley Heath and Hook Common	725530	65		•	•	•	•	•	•
Bourley Water	830502	152	MOD	•	•			•	
Eelmoor Marsh	840533	70.7	SSSI, RAE		•			•	•
Hazeley Heath	753583	175.7	SSSI, Common	•	•	•	•		•
Heckfield Heath	720620	75			•				
Long Valley	840520	350	MOD	•	•	•	•		
Newtown and Burghclere Commons	475627	10	SSSI, MOD, CC, Common, Common, Village Green	•					
Silchester Common	616611	38	SSSI, Common	•	•			•	
Tadley Common	606623	31.5		•			•		•
Yateley Common	833590	218	SSSI, Com, MOD	•	•		•	•	•
Western Weald									
Blackmoor	737333	32.3	SSSI	•					•
Bramshott & Ludshott	857345	378	SSSI, MOD, NT, Common	•			•	•	•
Broxhead Common	806374	34.5	SSSI, LNR, CC, Common	•					•
Canford Moor	821331	18.2	SSSI, NT, Common	•			•		•
Greatham Moor	782295	33	part MOD						
Kingsley Common	792381	45	MOD, Common	•			•	•	
Passfield Common	815335	20	NT, Common			•		•	•
Shortheath	775366	60	SSSI, MOD, Common	•			•	•	•
Slab Common	778350	120	Common, MOD	•				•	•
Woolmer Forest	795320	241	SSSI, MOD	•				•	•

*FC (Forestry Commission);
RAE (Royal Aircraft Establishment);
MOD (Ministry of Defence);
LNR (Local Nature Reserve)

NT (National Trust);
CC (County Council)

Appendix Three

Index to Scientific Names

Principal habitat (see key at end of list)

Adder — *Vipera berus*	1
Ants — *Lasius alienus and Tetramorium* caespitum	1
Lasius flavus and Myrmica sabuleti	4
Formica fusca and Myrmica ruginodis	5
Bell Heather — *Erica cinerea*	1
Bilberry — *Vaccinium myrtillus*	1
Bird's-foot — *Ornithopus perpusillus*	1
Bog Asphodel — *Narthecium ossifragum*	3
Bogbean — *Menyanthes trifoliata*	3
Bog Bush Cricket — *Metrioptera brachyptera*	3
Bog Myrtle — *Myrica gale*	3
Bog Rush — *Schoenus nigricans*	3
Bracken — *Pteridium aquilinum*	4
Bramble — *Rubus fruitcosus*	5
Bristle — (leaved) Bent — *Agrostis setecea*	1 or 4
Broom — *Sarothamnus scoparius*	5
Brown Beak-sedge — *Rhynchospora fusca*	2
Buzzard — *Buteo buteo*	5
Carnation Sedge — *Carex panicea*	2
Chaffinch — *Fringilla coelebs*	5
Cockroach — *Ectobius pallidus*	5
Common Butterwort — *Pinguicula vulgaris*	3
Common Sympetrum — *Sympetrum striolatum*	3
Common Lizard — *Lacerta vivipara*	1
Cotton Grass — *Eriophorum angustifolium*	3
Cranberry — *Vaccinium oxycoccus*	3
Creeping Bent — *Agrostis stolonifera*	4
Cross-leaved Heath — *Erica tetralix*	2
Curlew — *Numenius arquata*	2
Damsel flies — *Ischnura pumilio and* Ceriagrion tenellum	3
Dartford Warbler — *Sylvia undata*	1
Deergrass — *Scirpus cespitosus*	2
Dodder — *cuscuta epithymum*	1 or 4
Dorset Heath — *Erica ciliaris*	2
Dwarf Gorse — *Ulex minor*	2
Emperor Moth — *Saturnia pavonia*	1 or 5
European Gorse — *Ulex europeaus*	1 or 5
Four Spotted Libellula — *Libellula* quadrimaculata	3
Fox Moth — *Macrothylacia rubi*	1
Grass Emerald — *Pseudoterpna pruinata*	1
Grasshopper Warbler — *Locustella naevia*	5
Grayling — *Hipparchia semele*	4
Great Grey Shrike — *Lanius excubitor*	5
Green Hairstreak — *Callophrys rubi*	2
Green Tiger Beetle — *Cicindela campestris*	1
Golden Ringed Dragonfly — *Cordulegaster* boltonii	2
Gorse Shield Bug — *Piezodorus lituratus*	
Hare's-tail cotton-grass — *Eriophorum* vaginatum	✗ 2
Heath Assassin Bug — *Coranus subapterus*	1
Heath-grass — *Sieglingia decumbens*	2
Heath Grasshopper — *Chorthippus vagans*	2
Heath Milkwort — *Polygala serpyllifolia*	1 or 4
Heather — *Calluna vulgaris*	1
Heath Rush — *Juncus squarrosus*	2
Hen Harrier — *Circus cyaneus*	3
Hobby — *Falco subbuteo*	5
Ivy-leaved Bellflower — *Wahlenbergia* hederacea	4
Kestrel — *Falco tinnunculus*	5

Lapwing — *Vanellus vanellus*	4
Large Oak Eggar — *Lasiocampa quercus*	5 or 1
Lesser Bladderwort — *Utricularia minor*	3
Ling (Heather) — *Calluna vulgaris*	1
Marsh Cinquefoil — *Potentilla palustris*	3
Marsh Clubmoss — *Lycopodium inundatum*	2
Marsh Gentian — *Gentiana pneumonanthe*	2
Marsh Pennywort — *Hydrocotyle vulgaris*	3
Marsh Violet — *Viola palustris*	3
Meadow Pipit — *Anthus pratensis*	1
Merlin — *Falco columbarius*	1 or 2
Moor Mat-grass — *Nardus stricta*	4
Mossy Stonecrop — *Crassula tilloea*	1
Natterjack Toad — *Bufo calamita*	1
Narrow-winged Pug — *Eupithecia nanata*	1 or 2
Nightjar — *Caprimulgus europeaus*	1
Pale Butterwort — *Pinguicula lusitanica*	3
Pale Heath Violet — *Viola lactea*	2
Pine Hawk Moth — *Hyloicus pinastri*	5
Pink Crab Spider — *Thomisus onustus*	2
Potter Wasp — *Eumenes coarctara*	5 or 1
Purple Moor-grass — *Molinia caerulea*	4
Red-backed Shrike — *Lanius collurio*	1, 4 or 5
Redshank — *Tringa totanus*	2
Reed — *Phragmites communis*	3
Rosebay Willowherb — *Epilobium* angustifolium	3
Ruby Tiger — *Phragmatobia fuliginosa*	1 or 5
Sand Lizard — *Lacerta agilis*	1
Sand Wasp — *Ammophila sabulosa*	1
Sheep's Fescue — *Festuca ovina*	1
Silver-studded Blue — *Plebejus argus*	1
Skylark — *Alauda arvensis*	4
Smooth Snake — *Coronella austriaca*	1
Snipe — *Gallinago gallinago*	2
Sparrow Hawk — *Accipiter nisus*	5
Sphagnum Moss — *Sphagnum spp*	3
Stag's Horn Clubmoss — *Lycopodum clavatum*	5
Stonechat — *Saxicola torquata*	1
Sundews — *Drosera rotundifolia,* D.intermedia and D.anglica	3
Sweet Vernal Grass — *Anthoxanthum* odoratum	5
Tormentil — *Potentilla erecta*	1
Tree Pipit — *Anthus trivialis*	5
Upright Brome — *Bromus erectus*	chalk grassland
Wavy Hair Grass — *Deschampsia flexuosa*	1
Weasel — *Mustela nivalis*	5
Western Gorse — *Ulex gallii*	1
White Beak-sedge — *Rhynchospora alba*	3
Wild Gladiolus — *Gladiolus illyricus*	4
Wolf Spider — *Arctosa perita*	1
Woodlark — *Lullula arborea*	5
Wren — *Troglodytes troglodytes*	1
Yellow Bartsia — *Parentucellia viscosa*	3
Yorkshire Fog — *Holcus lanatus*	4

Key

Dry Heath	1
Wet or Humid Heath	2
Valley Bog	3
Acid Grass	4
Scrub Heath	5

26

References and Further Reading

1   Ecology of heathlands, by C.H. Gimingham; Chapman & Hall, London 1972

2   History of the British flora, by H. Godwin; Cambridge University Press 1975

3   The development of British heathlands and their soils. Oxford Forestry Memoir, 23. by G.W. Dimbleby, Clarendon, Oxford 1962

4   The vegetational history of south-east Dorset, Ph.D Thesis by L.E. Haskins; University of Southampton 1978

5   Vegetational History of the New Forest: A preliminary note, by K.E. Barber; Proceedings Hampshire Field Club Archaeological Society 1975

6   The Common Lands of Hampshire, by L.E. Tavener; Hampshire County Council 1957

7   Rural Rides, by W. Cobbett; Penguin Books 1967

8   Regional Studies on the British Lichen Flora, by F. Rose and P.W. James; The Lichenologist, Vol 6 1974

9   Victoria County History, Hampshire, Vol 3 1908

10 The Progress of a Ploughboy to a seat in Parliament, by W. Cobbett; ed. by William Reitzel

11 Conservation of the New Forest, Consultation Draft, 1970; Final Recommendations, 1971; Hampshire County Council

12 Heathlands of Western Europe, by O.W. Heal; Council of Europe, Strasbourg 1976

13 Upland land use in England and Wales, CCPIII; Countryside Commission, Cheltenham 1978

14 Nutrient budgets for a dry heath ecosystem in the south of England, by S.B. Chapman; Journal of Ecology, 55 1967

15 The establishment of seedlings on lowland heaths, by S.B. Chapman and R.J. Rose; Annual Report Institute Terrestrial Ecology 1979

16 Victoria County History, Hampshire, Vol 2 1884

17 Upland land use in England and Wales, CCPIII; Countryside Commission, Cheltenham 1978

FURTHER READING

Ecology of the Dartford warbler Sylvia undate (Boddaert) in relation to its conservation in Britain, by C.J. Bibby; Ph.D Thesis, CNAA 1977

The effect of spraying and respraying bracken (Pteridium aquilinum L. Kunn) in heathland with asolox, by J.L. Bostock; Bulletin of Ecology 11 1980

Changes in the species composition in an area dominated by Deschampsia flexuosa (1) Trin. as a result of cattle grazing, A. Bulow-Olsen; Biological Conservation 18 1980

Botanical implications of bracken control, by C.J. Cadbury; Botanical Journal of Linnaean Society 73 1976

Some relationships between soil, climate, standing crop and organic matter accumulation with a range of Calluna heathlands in Britain, by S.B. Chapman and R.T. Clarke; Bulletin of Ecology 11 1980

Net aerial production by Calluna vulgaris on lowland heath in Britain, by S.B. Chapman, Hibble and C.R. Rafarel; Journal of Ecology 63 1975(a)

Litter accumulation under Calluna vulgaris on a lowland heathland in Britain, by S.B. Chapman, Hibble and C.R. Rafarel; Journal of Ecology 63 1975(b)

The productivity of Calluna heathland in southern England, by S.B. Chapman and N.R. Webb; in Production ecology of some moors and montane grasslands, edited by O.W. Heal and D.F. Perking; Springer-Verlag, Berlin 1978

Sand lizards and their conservation, by K.F. Corbett; Sanctuary 8 1981

Conservation of the sand lizard, Lacerta agilis, by habitat management, by K.F. Corbett and D.L. Tamarind; British Journal of Herpetology 5 1979

Floristic analyses of British mires and mire communities, by R.E. Daniels; Journal of Ecology 66 1978

Limestone heaths in south-west Britain: their soils and the maintenance of their calcicole-calcifuge mixtures, by J.R. Etherington; Journal of Ecology 69 1981

Biological flora of the British Isles — Calluna vulgaris (L) Hull, by C.H. Gimingham; Journal of Ecology 48 1960

North European heath communities: a network of variation, by C.H. Gimingham; Journal of Ecology 49 1961

Conservation: European heathlands, by C.H. Gimingham; edited by R.L. Specht, Ecosystems of the world 9a, Elsevier, Amsterdam 1981

Reproduction as a factor in the conservation of Coronella austriaca Lavr., in southern England, by P. Goddard and I.F. Spellerbert; Bulletin of Ecology 11 1980

Nutrient cycling in heathlands, in Heathlands and related shrublands edited by R.L. Specht, by R.H. Groves; Ecosystems of the world 9a, Elsevier, Amsterdam 1981

The mechanism of acidification of soil by Calluna and Ulex and the significance for conservation, in The scientific management of animal and plant communities for conservation edited by E. Duffey and A.S. Watt, by P.J. Grubb and M.B. Suter; Blackwell, Oxford 1971

The ecology and conservation of British lowland heaths, in Conservation in practice, edited by A. Warren and F.B. Goldsmith, by C.M. Harrison; Wiley, London 1974

Heathland management in Surrey, England, by C.M. Harrison; Biological Conservation 10 1976

Preliminary results of field-wear trials of amenity grasslands and heathlands in south-east England, by C.M. Harrison; Bulletin of Ecology 11 1980

Some effects of fire and grazing on heath vegetation, by R.J. Hobbs and C.H. Gimingham; Bulletin of Ecology 11 1980

The management of grassland and heathland in country parks, by J.E. Lowday and T.C.E. Wells; CCP 105; Countryside Commission, Cheltenham 1977

Regeneration of heather (Calluna vulgaris (L) Hull) at different ages and seasons in north-east Scotland, by G.R. Miller and J. Miles; Journal of applied Ecology 7 1970

The heaths of Dorset and their conservation, by N.W. Moore; Journal of Ecology 50 1962

Ecology of the sand lizard (Lacerta agilis L.) in southern England and comparisons with the common lizard, by A.M. Nicholson; Ph.D Thesis, University of Southampton 1980

Heathlands of Western Europe, by A. Noirfalise and R. Vanesse; European Committee for the conservation of nature and natural resources, Council of Europe 1976

Vegetation (grasslands of England & Wales), Ordnance Survey Sheet 2, scale 1/625000 1945

The biology of bracken, by F.H. Perring and B.G. Gardiner (Eds); Botanical Journal of Linnaean Society 73 1976

A nature conservation review, by D. Ratcliffe (Ed.); Nature Conservancy Council and Natural Environment Research Council, Cambridge University Press

The conservation of the Dorset heaths — a factual study, by H.R.T. Rippey; M.Sc Thesis, University College, London 1973

A survey of the ecology of British lowland bogs, by F. Rose; Proceedings of the Linnaean Society 164 London 1953

Royal Commission on Common Land (1955-1958) Report HMSO Cmnd. 462

Heath fires in Dorset 1976, by RSPB and DNT; A report and recommendations by the Dorset Naturalist Trust and the Royal Society for the Protection of Birds, Sandy, Beds. 1977

Heathlands and related shrublands, by R.L. Specht (Ed.); *Ecosystems of the world 9a and 9b,* Elsevier, Amsterdam 1979 and 1981

An analysis of the sand lizard *(Lacerta agilis L.)* habitat in southern England, by I.F. Spellerberg and S.M. House; Unpublished report, University of Southampton 1980

The Common Lands of England and Wales, by A.L. Stamp and W.G. Hoskins; Collins 1963

Conservation in Surrey: An appraisal of selected open spaces, by Surrey County Council; Kingston upon Thames 1970

Southern Heathlands, by Surrey Trust for Nature Conservation; Report of Symposium 1974

Heath fires in Surrey 1976, by Surrey Trust for Nature Conservation and Royal Society for the Protection of Birds; Sandy, Beds 1976

The British Isles and their vegetation, A.G. Tansley; Cambridge University Press, Cambridge 1939

The New Forest: an ecological history, by C.R. Tubbs; David and Charles, Newton Abbot 1968

Heathland management in the New Forest, Hampshire, England, by C.R. Tubbs; *Biological Conservation 6* 1974

The Dorset heathlands: present status and conservation, by N.R. Webb; *Bulletin of Ecology 11* 1980

An ecological survey of heathlands in the Poole Basin, Dorset, England in 1978, by N.R. Webb and L.E. Haskins; *Biological Conservation 17* 1980

The natural history of Selborne by G. White; B. White, London 1789

The management of heathlands for amenity purposes in south-east England, by E.M. Yates; *Geographica Polonica, 24.* Warsaw 1972

Status, habitats and conservation of the Dartford warbler in England, by C.J. Bibby & C.R. Tubbs; *British Birds, 68* 1975

The heaths of Dorset and their conservation, by N.W. Moore; *Journal of Ecology 50* 1962

An Ecological Survey of Heathlands in the Poole Basin, Dorset, England, in 1978 by N.R. Webb and L.E. Haskins; *Biological Conservation 17* 1980

The Conservation of the Dorset Heaths – a factual study by B.H.R.T. Rippey; MSc Thesis, University College London 1973